Asterix and the big fight

Gaul was divided into three parts.
No, four parts – for one small village of
indomitable Gauls still held out against
the Roman invaders . . .

Asterix the Gaul and his friend
Obelix are involved in further
humorous adventures in their
efforts to secure their tribe from
a particularly devious Roman
threat.
'. . . the English rendering is as
brilliant as ever. . .Even the most
familiar of situations is hilarious,
so spirited and brisk is the folly.'
Times Literary Supplement

SHAKESPEARE AND COMPANY KILOMETER ZERO PARIS

TEXT BY GOSCINNY

Asterix and the big fight

DRAWINGS BY UDERZO

Translated by Anthea Bell and

Derek Hockridge

KNIGHT BOOKS
Hodder & Stoughton

ISBN 0 340 17937 6
Copyright © 1966 Dargaud Editeur
English-language text copyright © 1971 Hodder & Stoughton Limited
First published in Great Britain in 1971 by Brockhampton Press Ltd
This edition first published in 1974 by Knight, the paperback division of
Brockhampton Press Ltd (now Hodder & Stoughton Children's Books),
Salisbury Road, Leicester
Third impression 1976

Printed and bound in Great Britain by
Richard Clay (The Chaucer Press) Ltd, Bungay, Suffolk

This book is sold subject to the condition that it shall not by
way of trade or otherwise be lent, re-sold, hired out or otherwise
circulated without the publisher's prior consent in any form of
binding or cover other than that in which this is published and
without a similar condition including this condition being imposed
on the subsequent purchaser.

The year is 50 BC. Gaul is entirely occupied
by the Romans. Well, not entirely...
One small village of indomitable Gauls still
holds out against the invaders. And life is not easy for the
Roman legionaries who garrison the fortified camps of
Totorum, Aquarium, Laudanum and Compendium...

Now turn the book sideways
and read on...

a few of the Gauls

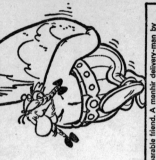

Obelix, Asterix's inseparable friend. A menhir delivery-man by trade; addicted to wild boar. Obelix is always ready to drop everything and go off on a new adventure with Asterix – so long as there's wild boar to eat, and plenty of fighting.

Asterix, the hero of these adventures. A shrewd, cunning little warrior; all perilous missions are immediately entrusted to him. Asterix gets his superhuman strength from the magic potion brewed by the druid Getafix...

Getafix, the venerable village druid. Gathers mistletoe and brews magic potions. His speciality is the potion which gives the drinker superhuman strength. But Getafix also has other recipes up his sleeve...

Finally, Vitalstatistix, the chief of the tribe. Majestic, brave and hot-tempered, the old warrior is respected by his men and feared by his enemies. Vitalstatistix himself has only one fear; he is afraid the sky may fall on his head tomorrow. But as he always says, 'Tomorrow never comes.'

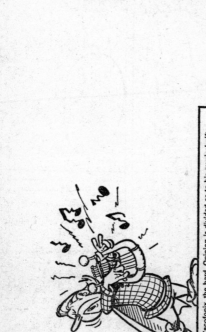

Cecofonix, the bard. Opinion is divided as to his musical gifts. Cecofonix thinks he's a genius. Everyone else thinks he's unspeakable. But so long as he doesn't speak, let alone sing, everybody likes him....

GNNNNEE HEEHEE!

HOWA! HA HA! HA HA!

HEY... WHAT ABOUT ME?

ALL IS WELL! THAT MENIR OBVIOUSLY MADE SOME IMPACT ON THE DRUID! HE HAS LOST HIS POWERS FOR MAKING MAGIC POTION!

LET'S GET AT THE GAULS! THERE ARE A LOT MORE OF US THAN THEM!

IT'S QUITE UNNECESSARY TO RISK INJURY... LET CASSIUS CERAMIX DO THE DIRTY WORK FOR US. WE'LL ATTACK ONLY IF HE LOSES!

DON'T WORRY! THE EFFECTS OF THESE GAULISH POTIONS ARE ONLY TEMPORARY! IT WILL SOON WEAR OFF. HAVE A GOOD NIGHT!

WHAT'S TO BECOME OF ME! YOU'RE STARTING TO GET ME DOWN... I HOPE!

HE FLIES AT NIGHT, JUST LIKE ME! HE'S THE NICEST THING I EVER LIGHTED UPON!

WHAT'S UP WITH YOU?

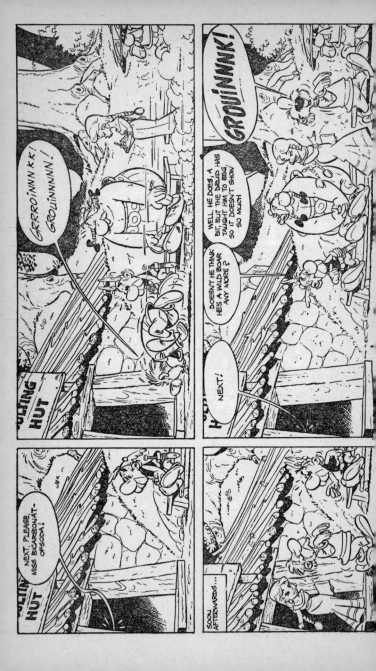

SOON AFTERWARDS... I KNOW SOME VERY CLEVER TRICKS WITH A CAULDRON TOO!

NOW REMEMBER, WHATEVER YOU DO DON'T CONTRADICT THE PATIENT

PUT MY CAULDRON ON TO BOIL... IT LOOKS AS THOUGH I'LL HAVE TO MAKE SOME POTIONS

OBELIX! DON'T BE SO PIG-HEADED. IT DOESN'T TAKE A DRUID TO KNOW THAT IT WAS ALL ON ACCOUNT OF YOUR MENHIR!

I DON'T THINK IT WAS THAT AT ALL. YOU ALWAYS MAKE OUT IT WAS MY FAULT. YOU'RE NOT GOING TO TELL ME THAT A LITTLE TAP WITH A...

WHAT HAPPENED TO HIM? SOME SORT OF A SHOCK?

YES, IT WAS A MENHIR GOT HIM DOWN

WHILE THE COMBATANTS ARE IN TRAINING, THE ROMANS BUILD THE RING FOR THE BIG FIGHT OUTSIDE THE CAMP...

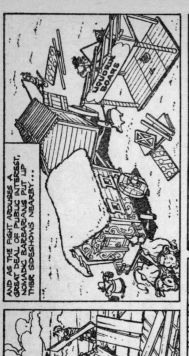

AND AS THE FIGHT AROUSES A GREAT DEAL OF PUBLIC INTEREST, NOMADIC BARBARIANS PUT UP THEIR SIDESHOWS NEARBY...

LIQUIDRUM BOARS

SHOOTING RANGE
5 BULLS-EYES WINS A JAR OF BULLS-EYES

CATAPULTS
1 BRONZE
WINS A
GOBI

SPEARS
2 BRONZE
COINS A
THROW

DODGEM CHARIOTS

1ˢ

1 SESTERTIUS

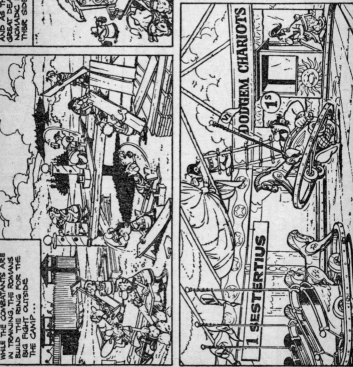

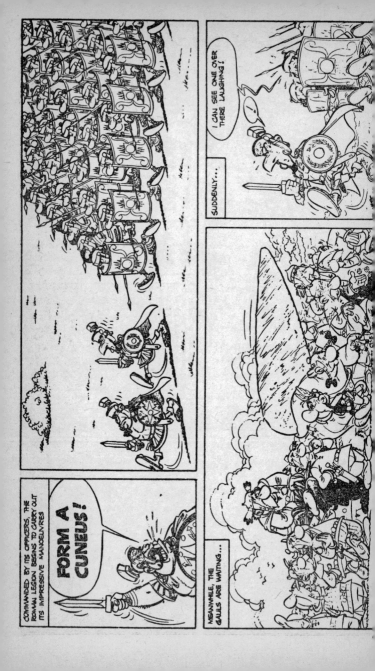

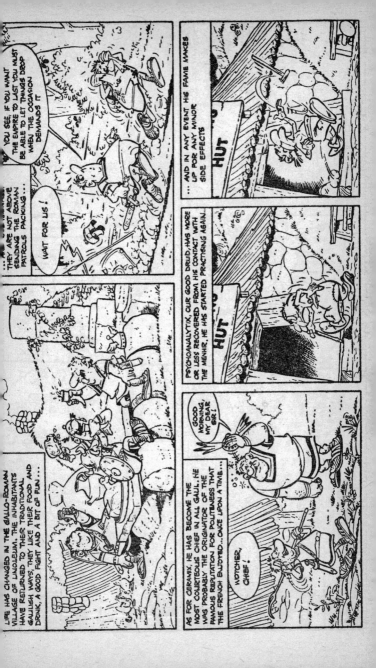

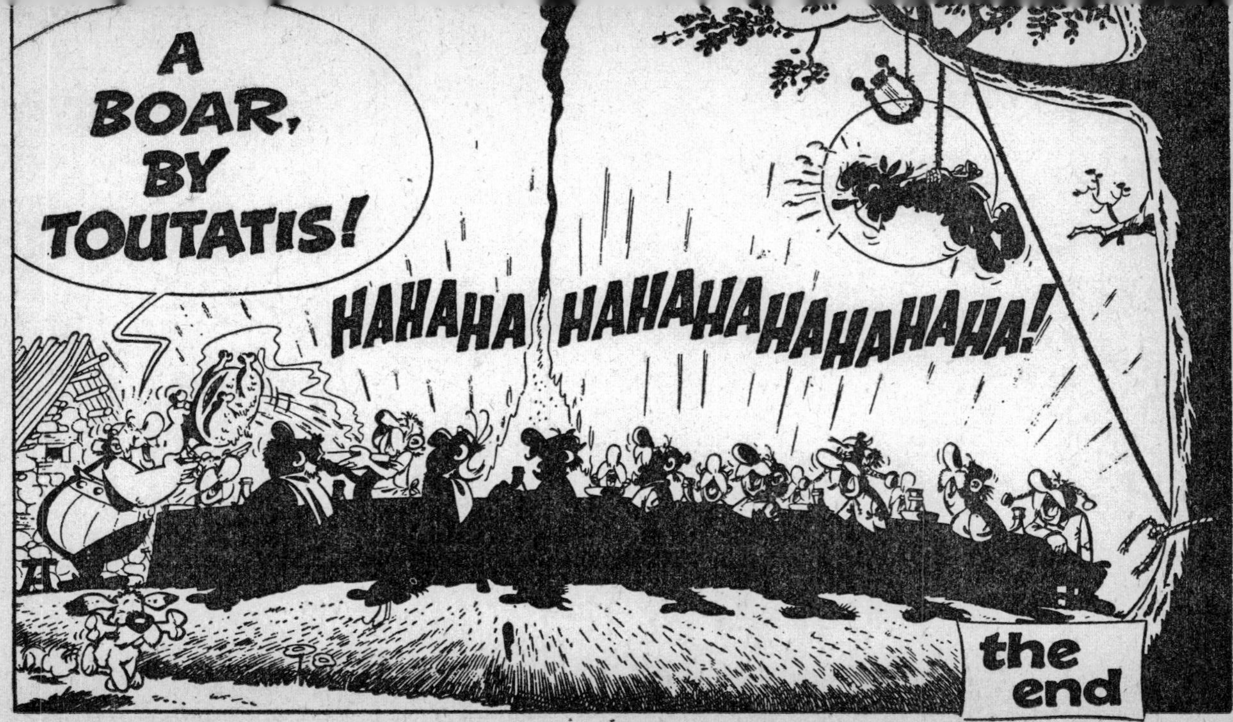
A BOAR, BY TOUTATIS!
HAHAHA HAHAHAHAHAHAHAHA!
the end